Southborough Library
Tel 01892 529808
Fax 01892 540442
southboroughlibrary@kent.gov.uk
- 8 NOV 2011
11/10
15 JUL 2011
WITHDRAWN
12 FEB 2011
Please return on or before the latest date above.
You can renew online at www.kent.gov.uk/libs
or by phone 08458 247 200
CHARTER MARK
CUSTOMER SERVICE EXCELLENCE
Libraries & Archives
Kent County Council

C155287705

Toot!
Sssshh!
Just one more sweetie...
Me too!

True. *Very true.*

Dear Reader,

If you read the Old Testament of the Holy Bible, you will find that it is packed full of brilliant and exciting stories. In this book I have chosen my favourites. They are:

They are simply divine!

I have spent many happy hours retelling and illustrating these stories and I hope they will give you many happy hours of reading and looking.

Marcia Williams

P.S. The words spoken by God are taken from the New International Version of the Bible. All the others are my own, inspired by reading this version.

First published 2004 as *God and His Creations*
by Walker Books Ltd, 87 Vauxhall Walk, London SE11 5HJ

This edition published 2010

10 9 8 7 6 5 4 3 2 1

This book has been typeset in Phaistos Bold

Printed in China

British Library Cataloguing in Publication Data:
a catalogue record for this book is available from the British Library

ISBN 978-1-4063-2610-9

www.walker.co.uk

For Oscar,
Hettie and Abel,
with love

Noah's Ark and Other Bible Stories

retold and illustrated by
Marcia Williams

WALKER BOOKS
AND SUBSIDIARIES
LONDON • BOSTON • SYDNEY • AUCKLAND

GOD'S CREATIONS
Don't forget us, the angels.
Mind my toe!
LET
THERE BE
LIGHT!
God's feet (as seen for the first time).
In the beginning there was only God. The earth was formless and dark.
DAY!
NIGHT!
DAY!
NIGHT!
Look, it's me!
Then God created light! He called the light "day", and the darkness "night" – on that first day.
SKY!
He's on a roll!
On the second day God created space to divide the waters. He called it "sky".
RIVERS!
SEAS!
LAND!
PLANTS AND TREES!
On the third day God made rivers, seas, and dry land that was rich in plants and trees.
THIS IS ALL ...
VERY GOOD!
Pretty!
God put the sun, the moon and the stars in the sky.
So there was evening, and there was morning – on that fourth day.
Wow! An orb-ball.

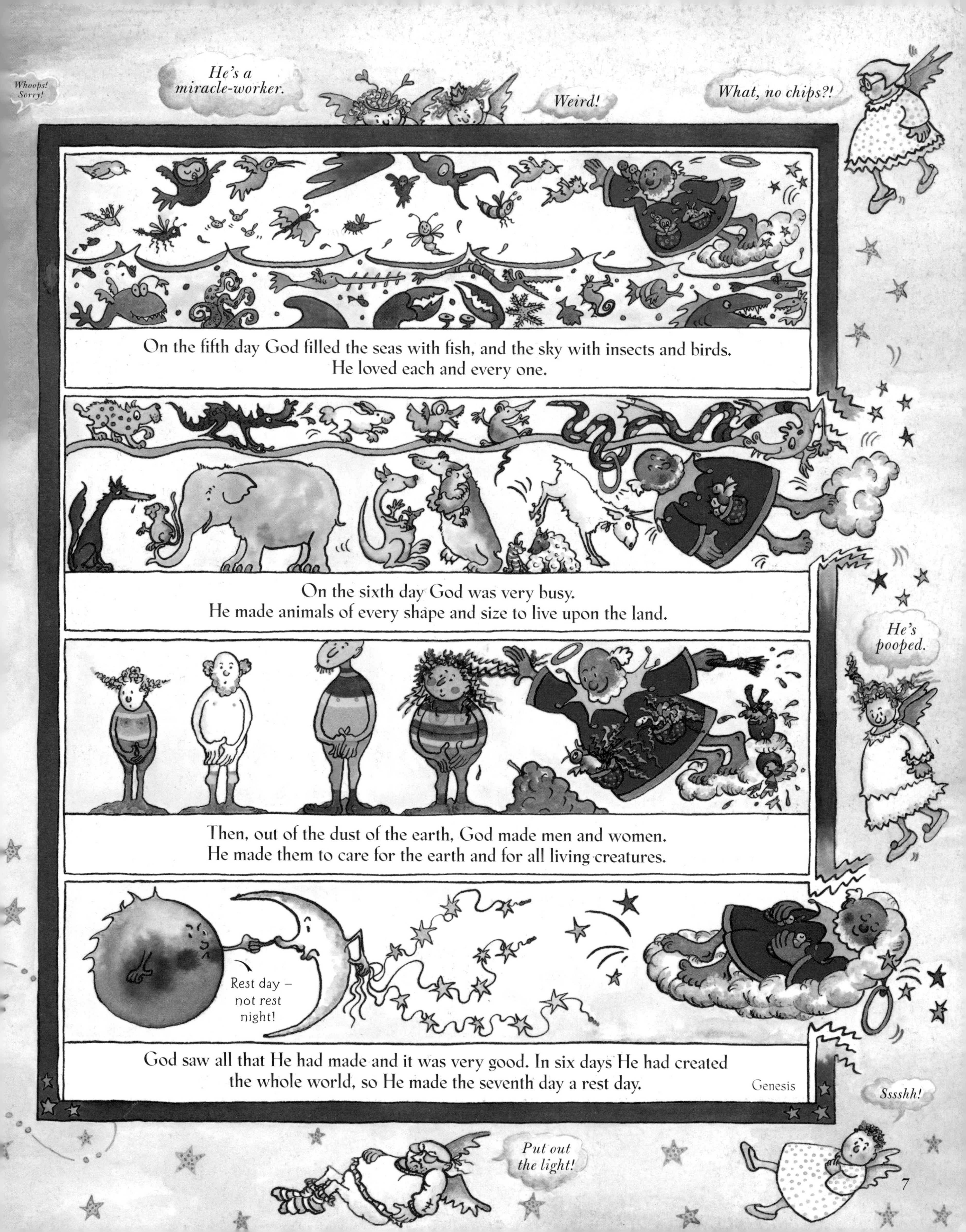
Whoops! Sorry!
He's a miracle-worker.
Weird!
What, no chips?!
On the fifth day God filled the seas with fish, and the sky with insects and birds.
He loved each and every one.
On the sixth day God was very busy.
He made animals of every shape and size to live upon the land.
He's pooped.
Then, out of the dust of the earth, God made men and women.
He made them to care for the earth and for all living creatures.
Rest day – not rest night!
God saw all that He had made and it was very good. In six days He had created the whole world, so He made the seventh day a rest day.
Genesis
Sssshh!
Put out the light!

THE GARDEN OF EDEN

The first man God breathed life into was Adam. God planted a garden called Eden for Adam to live in. God told Adam to enjoy all the fruits of Eden, except for those from the tree of the knowledge of good and evil – for if he tasted these, he would die. Adam obeyed God, for he loved Him. But when God was not with him in the garden, Adam felt lonely.

Bit too bony?
She's angelic.
Angelic, my wing!
This is now bone of my bones.
We will never want for more.
So, while Adam slept, God took a rib from his side.
From the rib of Adam, God made the first woman, Eve.
For some time Adam and Eve lived contentedly in Eden.
No!
You will surely not die if you eat this fruit.
Your eyes will be opened.
No!
Yes!
But a crafty serpent spoke to Eve beside the tree of knowledge.
He told her that its fruit would make her as wise as God.
So Eve took fruit from the tree of knowledge, and ate it.
I'll be back!
Mmm, yummy.
My body is uncovered!
Mine too!
He made me.
Cursed are you...
Then she gave some fruit to Adam, and he ate it.
At once they became ashamed of their nakedness.
God angrily condemned the serpent to crawl upon his belly.
By the sweat of your brow you will eat your food.
NO RE-ENTRY
Poor God. He's gutted!
He cast Adam and Eve out of Eden and set an angel to guard the gate. From then on Adam and Eve had to fend for themselves, where thorns and thistles grew and animals were savage. But God still cared for them and the many children born to them. But, as He had predicted, Adam and Eve did eventually die – although not until they were very, very old.
Genesis
They were too greedy!

Nice!
Not nice.
NOAH'S ARK
Fat, thin, tall or short, God loves us all.
Over the years, men and women grew in number.
Biff! Bang!
We covet our neighbours' goods.
But their ways became wicked and cruel.
I am going to put an end to all people...
So God decided to destroy them in a great flood.
Quite right.
...I am surely going to destroy both them and the earth.
All except for Noah and his family, for Noah was a good, kind man.
God told Noah to build an ark of cypress wood, three storeys high, with a door in the side.
Be a rebel, Noah. Fill it with ssserpents.
...every kind of food...
Hay for the camels.
Hay! Hay! Hay!
Hay for the sheep.
Noah and his family worked hard. When the ark stood strong and watertight God told Noah to fill it with food. So he and his family plucked, gathered and baked until the shelves were overflowing.
Yum.
A falling angel.

Then God told Noah to fill the ark with a male and female of every living creature. So he and his family chased, herded and coaxed until the ark was loaded. As the first drops of rain began to fall, God slammed the great door shut and bolted it firmly.

God's ever so cross.
Call me when the rain stops.
The rain poured down and the waters rose. The loaded ark was lifted above the earth. Soon no other creatures were left alive, and the highest mountain was covered with water.
Hay for breakfast.
Hay for lunch.
Hay for dinner.
Hay today!
Hay tomorrow!
Haytime.
Hay! Hay! Hay!
Quack, quack!
Baa, baa!
Burp, burp!
Wet? What nonsense!
Mmm ... hay today!
Yuk!
Hay every day.
Yuk every day!
Hay ...
hay, hay ...
and more ...
HAY!
Yum, yum!
Neigh!
Rotten hay!
Wet hay!
Dry hay!
Leftover hay!
Forever hay!
Dream of...
Bananas!
Flies!
Grapes!
Bones!
Carrots!
Salad!
Cheese!
Snails!
Berries!
Nuts!
Noah's toes!
Noah's toes?
Noah's toes!
Munch gulp (x10!)
For forty days and forty nights the rain fell. The ark floated on the swirling waters.
Sssoppy umbrellas.
Help! My wings are waterlogged.

Thank God it's stopped raining!
I already did.
The rain's stopped.
Until at last God sent a wind over the earth. The rain ceased and the waters began to recede.
Why me?
The ark came to rest on Mt Ararat. Noah let out a raven, but it found nowhere to land.
Careful, we're tipping.
I need a towel.
A few days later Noah sent out a dove. It flew for miles, but could find nowhere to rest its feet.
Their hay-days are over.
Thank God!
Seven days later Noah sent out the dove again. In the evening it returned with an olive branch.
We made it!
After another seven days the dove flew out again. It did not return, because the earth had dried.
What a wet tale.
Noah opened the great doors of the ark and out rushed his family and all God's creatures. Noah built an altar to thank God, and God was delighted. He promised Noah never to flood the world again, and He set a rainbow in the sky as a sign of His promise.
Genesis
Handy things, umbrellas!

ABRAHAM AND ISAAC
Snore!
Leave your country...
Of course.
Must we? He's so old.
You're no spring chicken either!
We're n-o-o-o-t g-o-o-ing.
You'll do as I tell you.
After Noah, there was a shepherd named Abraham who loved God above everything else. When God asked him to travel to Canaan with his wife Sarah, he did not hesitate.
Quick, Sarah, bake some bread.
OK, but NO more moving.
When they reached Canaan, God visited them again.
Sarah your wife will have a son.
I'm a hundred years old!
I'm worn out!
He told Abraham and Sarah that they would have a son.
God's little joke!
They laughed, thinking they were too old to have a child.
God doesn't do jokes.
God's precious gift.
God has brought me laughter.
But the next year, as God had said, Sarah gave birth to a boy.
Come to Daddy, Isaac.
You can do it!
They named him Isaac and he grew healthy and strong.
Daddy's little helper.
Bless him.
Abraham and Sarah were very proud; they loved Isaac dearly.
Take your son, your only son Isaac.
Come on, Dad won't sacrifice you!
So when God asked Abraham to sacrifice Isaac as a burnt offering, Abraham thought his heart would break. But he collected wood, some fire and a sacrificial knife and set out with his son.
Huh! He's only losing a son – I lost my wings!
Oh dear.

Life does have its downs.
I blame Adam and Eve.
I blame the serpent.
Father? The fire and the wood are here, but where is the lamb for the burnt offering?
God Himself will provide the lamb.
After three days Abraham and Isaac reached the place that God had chosen for the sacrifice.
I can't look!
Abraham! Do not lay a hand on the boy.
I will surely bless you and make your descendants as numerous as the stars in the sky...
Abraham bound Isaac and placed him on top of an altar. But, as he raised the knife, an angel stopped him. God had been testing Abraham and now He was sure that Abraham loved Him above all else. God promised Abraham that his descendants would be leaders of great nations.
Yuk! Another happy ending.
God spoke to me!
Luckily for me!
That's nice, dear, but I'm not moving again.
Nor me!
No-o-o-r us!
Abraham and Isaac returned joyfully home to Canaan to tell Sarah of God's great promise.
Genesis
What are descendants?
Your children and your children's children and your children's children's children...

JOSEPH AND HIS FABULOUS ROBE
Twelve boys – what perfection!
What about new wings for me?
I remember when you were a boy, Isaac.
Dad, Gramps, I've brought the boys to see you.
Isaac, the son of Abraham, stayed in Canaan and had twin sons of his own, Esau and Jacob. Jacob became a farmer and had twelve sons.
That's my boy!
It's fab! Thanks, Dad.
It stinks!
Jacob loved his sons, but especially Joseph. He gave him a new robe. Joseph's brothers were jealous and began to hate him.
God's had a hand in this.
Then Joseph had two strange dreams. In the first, Joseph and his brothers were binding corn.
Suddenly Joseph's sheaf rose and stood upright and his brothers' sheaves bowed down before it.
Sweet dreams!
In the second dream the sun, the moon and eleven stars bowed down before him as though he were king.
We must keep this matter in mind, my dearest boy!
He thinks he'll actually rule us. No chance – baa!
His father believed the dreams meant that Joseph would become a ruler. His brothers' hatred grew. They stormed off to tend the sheep.
Sorry! Angels only up here.
You're my favourite doll.

It doesn't pay to have a new robe.
Rescue him, someone!
Here comes that dreamer! Come now, let's kill him.
Hey, bros!
Jacob sent Joseph to join his brothers. But when they saw him coming, the brothers plotted to kill him. All except Reuben.
Let's not take his life, but throw him into this cistern.
We'll say some wild animal killed him.
He persuaded the others not to kill Joseph, but just to take his fine robe and cast him into an empty well instead.
Ssssplendid!
Come, let's sell him to the Ishmaelites and not lay our hands on him. After all, he is our brother.
But then a caravan of Ishmaelites came towards them, carrying spices to trade in Egypt. The brothers sold Joseph to them for a bag of silver. They dipped Joseph's robe in animal blood and returned home.
Ah, bless!
In mourning will I go down to the grave to my son.
Jacob believed that wild beasts had killed Joseph. He rent his clothes, put on sackcloth and mourned.
Is that what's called brotherly love?
Well, it's not sisterly!

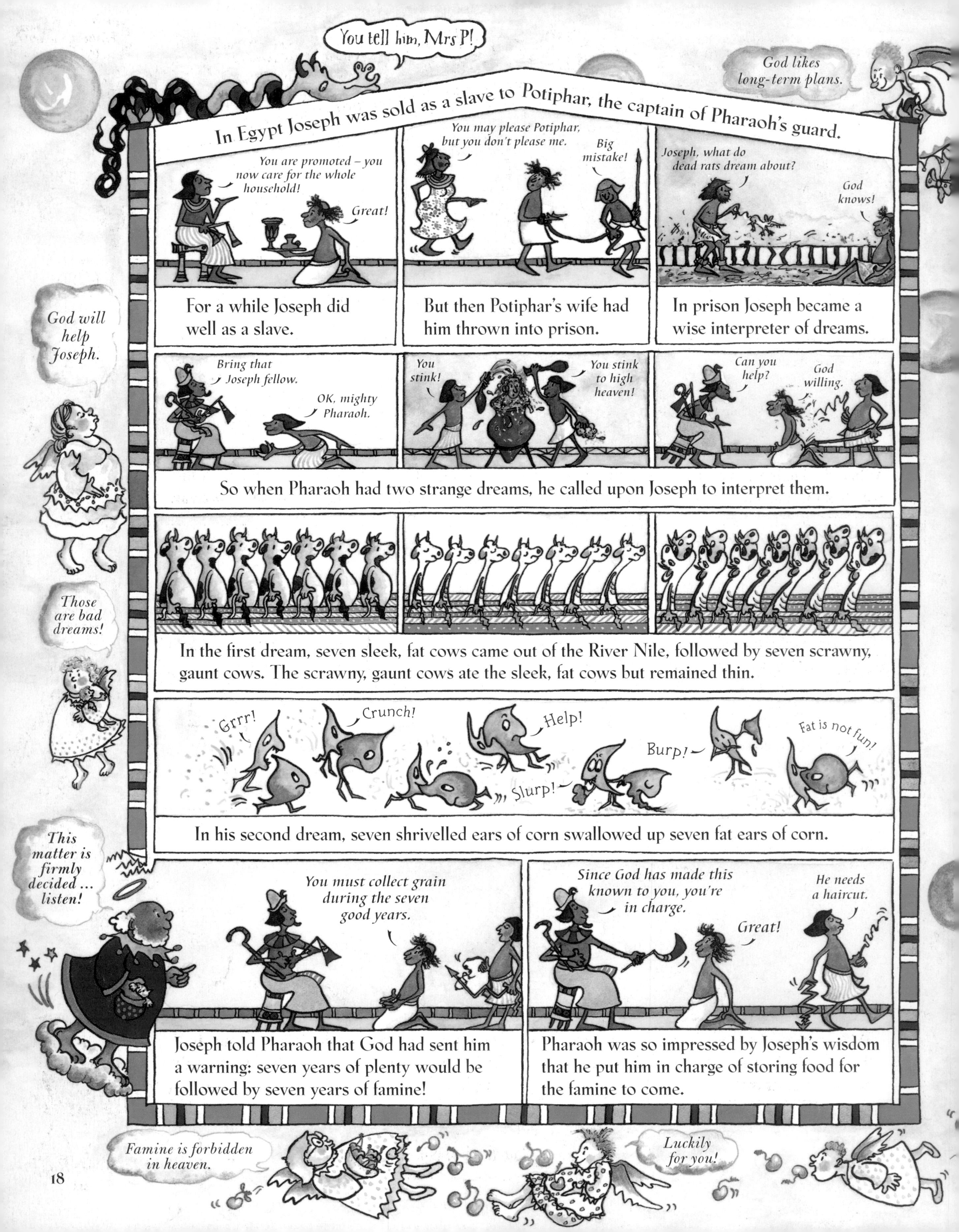
You tell him, Mrs P!
God likes long-term plans.
In Egypt Joseph was sold as a slave to Potiphar, the captain of Pharaoh's guard.
You are promoted – you now care for the whole household!
Great!
For a while Joseph did well as a slave.
You may please Potiphar, but you don't please me.
Big mistake!
But then Potiphar's wife had him thrown into prison.
Joseph, what do dead rats dream about?
God knows!
In prison Joseph became a wise interpreter of dreams.
God will help Joseph.
Bring that Joseph fellow.
OK, mighty Pharaoh.
You stink!
You stink to high heaven!
Can you help?
God willing.
So when Pharaoh had two strange dreams, he called upon Joseph to interpret them.
Those are bad dreams!
In the first dream, seven sleek, fat cows came out of the River Nile, followed by seven scrawny, gaunt cows. The scrawny, gaunt cows ate the sleek, fat cows but remained thin.
Grrr!
Crunch!
Help!
Slurp!
Burp!
Fat is not fun!
In his second dream, seven shrivelled ears of corn swallowed up seven fat ears of corn.
This matter is firmly decided ... listen!
You must collect grain during the seven good years.
Joseph told Pharaoh that God had sent him a warning: seven years of plenty would be followed by seven years of famine!
Since God has made this known to you, you're in charge.
Great!
He needs a haircut.
Pharaoh was so impressed by Joseph's wisdom that he put him in charge of storing food for the famine to come.
Famine is forbidden in heaven.
Luckily for you!

His brothers would be jealous.
Maybe they've mended their ways.
Wake me when the famine's over.
Pharaoh gave Joseph many treasures and made him governor of all Egypt.
Tally-ho!
You can tell he's not from Egypt.
A fifth of your harvest and no cheating!
Call that a haircut?
There were seven years of abundance before the terrible famine struck across many lands. During these years Joseph had storehouses built and collected vast mounds of grain.
It's your brother, sillies!
Watch out for little Benjamin.
OK, Dad.
Well, well, just like my dream.
We come from Canaan to buy food.
When the famine came there was only grain in Egypt, and Joseph's brothers travelled there all the way from Canaan to buy food. They did not recognize Joseph, but he recognized them straight away.
They're all mad!
You shall be my slave.
Me?
No, take me!
No, me! I'm so humble!
What about me?
Me! I'm brainy.
We're the tallest.
I'm the strongest!
Wow! A whole orb-ball team!
Joseph decided to test his brothers, to see if they were still wicked. He threatened to enslave Benjamin, the youngest. The brothers knew how much this would upset their father and so they pleaded to be enslaved instead. Joseph saw by this that his brothers had changed.
Well, there's a turn-up for the papyrus!
It's me, Joseph, and I love you!
With great joy he made himself known to them. He bade them fetch his father Jacob and settle in Egypt.
Three cheers for Joseph!
Welcome to Egypt, Dad.
My favourite boy.
Hip, hip, hip!
The Egyptians and Joseph's family all survived the famine – thanks to God, who had brought Joseph to Egypt.
Genesis
You thief of wings!

Trouble comes next, O Israel.
THE STORY OF MOSES
Your name will be Israel.
A new name at my age – what next!
Before Jacob died, God changed his name to Israel, and his descendants – Joseph and his brothers, and their children, and their children's children – became known as the Israelites.
The Israelites have become too numerous. Make them slaves.
Good plan, mighty Pharaoh.
When they give birth, if it's a boy, kill him!
Even better plan, mighty Pharaoh.
The Israelites became so rich and numerous in Egypt that the Pharaoh began to fear their power. He made them slaves, and ordered the death of all their baby boys.
Poor, lonely baby.
This must be an Israelite baby.
Yummy fish!
To save her son, one Israelite mother hid her baby among the reeds by the bank of the Nile. Pharaoh's daughter found him there when she came to bathe. She named the baby Moses and took him home to live with her as her son.
Carry the whole pyramid, not just one brick!
Stop that.
Run, Moses, or Daddy will kill you!
I'm out of here!
God must have plans for Moses.
Moses knew that his parents were Israelites, and, as he grew older, he tried to protect other Israelites. One day he killed an Egyptian for giving an Israelite slave a cruel beating, and so he was forced to flee from Egypt.
Know-all!
I hope his luck holds out.

That'll be tough.
God'll help!
Far away from Pharaoh's wrath Moses found work as a shepherd. But God had a job for him.
Who am I? Why would Pharaoh listen to me?
I will be with you.
One day God spoke to Moses from a burning bush. He told Moses to fetch the Israelites from Egypt into a better land. But Moses was afraid that this task would be too difficult for him.
Gulp!
Grrrr.
God told Moses to throw down his staff. It became a snake.
When God told Moses to pick the snake up by the tail, it became a staff again.
Bother, bother, bother, bother!
God told Moses to put his hand inside his cloak. His hand turned sickly white.
When he replaced his hand inside his cloak, it was healed.
I still think God should send some other poor soul!
Me too!
Yoo-hoo! Moses, I've made a map!
EGYPT FROM THE SKY
God said signs like these would convince Pharaoh to let the Israelites go. He told Moses not to be afraid. At last Moses obeyed, and set out for Egypt with the staff of God in his hand.
Goal!

In Egypt Moses asked Pharaoh to release the Israelites. He showed God's signs with his staff.
Let the Israelites go.
No, no, no, no, no! They are my slaves and I need them.
A plague of serpents would do it.
But Pharaoh would not listen. So God sent plagues, as more signs, to persuade him.
Yuk, and NO!
God turned all the water of Egypt into blood.
I shall keep my slaves!
He made a plague of frogs hop across the land.
No!
He turned the dust of Egypt into gnats.
They may NOT leave!
Allow me to help with my heavenly fly swat!
He sent swarms of big, buzzing flies.
What, no meat?
I'll keep my slaves and eat fish!
He visited a terrible disease upon all Egyptian animals.
I – ouch! – will not – aagh! – let them – oh the agony! – LEAVE!
He tortured the Egyptian people with festering boils.
Ouch! Oooh!
No!
He battered them with huge hailstones.
I can live without bread, but not my slaves.
He sent millions of locusts to destroy their crops.
NO!
He covered all of Egypt in darkness.
I'm glad we're up here and not down there.
Up! LEAVE my people, you and the Israelites!
Your wish is our command.
Finally God took the life of the eldest boy in every Egyptian family, even Pharaoh's.
Now Pharaoh listened. He told Moses to take the Israelites out of his land, out of Egypt.
You've been told before ...
... this is a forbidden zone!
Can you play orb-ball?

Look how many are going.
How will the Egyptians build pyramids without them?
You'll need a miracle to get out of this!
God showed Moses the way out, with a pillar of cloud in the day and a pillar of fire at night.
But soon Pharaoh wanted his slaves back. He sent his army after the Israelites and trapped them at the edge of the Red Sea. But God sent a wind to part the sea, and Moses led them to safety.
I'm not impressed.
When the Egyptians tried to follow, the sea poured back, covering the whole army. At last the Israelites were free, and, led by Moses, they began their long journey through the desert.
Where's my manna from heaven?
God is so good, rain down bread.
It gets a bit boring after forty years!
When they were hungry, God fed them. When they were thirsty, God gave them water. And in this way they travelled bravely for many years towards the land that God had promised them.
Exodus
Too much walking!
LAND OF MILK AND HONEY THIS WAY

THE BATTLE OF JERICHO

By the time the Israelites reached the River Jordan, Moses was too old to travel further. So God gave them a new leader, a soldier named Joshua. God sent an angel to tell Joshua how to destroy the city of Jericho, which stood between the Israelites and their Promised Land. Once a day for six days Joshua marched his army in silence around the walls of Jericho. Seven priests went with them, sounding their trumpets and carrying the golden ark that held the ten commandments which God had given to Moses.

On the seventh day the procession marched around the closed city seven times. On the seventh time, when the priests gave one long trumpet blast, the soldiers all gave a great war cry – and the walls of Jericho collapsed before them. Then the soldiers charged in and burned the whole city and everything in it. God was with Joshua and the Israelites that day, and their fame spread far and wide. Now they were free to live in the land He had promised to Moses so long ago.

Joshua

Go on, Philistines, attack!
SAMSON AND DELILAH
Not one Philistine attack the whole night!
They won't attack in the heat of the day.
Don't bet on that!
After the fall of Jericho the Israelites settled in the Promised Land. But they had to fight to keep it, and sometimes they lost and were ruled over by other nations, such as the Philistines.
Oopsy!
Oof!
Yelp!
Aaah!
Oooh!
Yikes!
But God sent numerous leaders to help the Israelites. And the strongest was Samson. He once killed a thousand Philistine soldiers with just the jawbone of a donkey.
That's between Samson and God.
My sugar-plum.
Get us the secret of his strength.
The Philistines feared Samson and wanted to know how he could be subdued, so they bribed Delilah, his love, to find out.
Philistines, I've got him!
BOO!
LIAR!
Delilah cajoled Samson into telling her that being tied by seven green thongs would weaken him – but it did not.
SNORE! SNORE!
After more cajoling, Samson said that weaving his hair would weaken him – but it did not.
Boo! I'm as strong as ever!
You've made a fool of me!
Delilah became so angry that Samson decided he had better tell her the truth!
Where is God?
Here, there and everywhere!

My strength is in my shoes!
Naughty Delilah.
I'm rooting for you, Samson.
I'll give you lots of silver if this works.
It'll work.
That night a Philistine shaved Samson's head. As his hair fell about the bed, his strength left him.
Wait until my hair grows.
The cruel Philistines blinded Samson and set him to work in a lonely prison.
What a waste!
Months later, the Philistine rulers gathered in their temple and called for Samson. They planned to taunt him. But Samson's hair had grown again and he asked the jailer to stand him near two pillars. Calling upon God's help, he pushed against the pillars with all his might until the temple came down, burying all the people in it. And so Samson died with his enemies.
Judges
Don't you hate a show-off?
Poor Samson.
Humans are too active. Zzzz...

I'm with you, Goliath!
DAVID AND GOLIATH
They have rejected me as their king.
We need a proper king to fight the Philistines.
Me, I'm the tallest.
OK – Saul for King! Long live King Saul!
Forward march ... HALT!
Behold! An Israelite gnome!
The Israelites had many leaders, but no king except God. Until they crowned Saul.
King Saul was to help them fight the Philistines and their giant warrior, Goliath.
Kill me and we will be your subjects.
Fat chance.
I will give great wealth to the man who kills him – great, great wealth; great, great, great wealth.
Come on, you wimps!
The fearful Goliath challenged King Saul to find a soldier to fight him in single combat.
King Saul offered many fine rewards, but no Israelite dared to fight the giant.
For forty days and forty nights Goliath took his stand, but still no soldier volunteered.
Big bully!
Who is he to defy the armies of the living God?
Cowards!
I will go and fight him.
You?!
God will deliver me.
Oh well, if you say so.
David, a shepherd boy, heard Goliath's challenge while taking food to his soldier brothers.
David was enraged. Goliath's challenge was an insult to God. So he offered to fight.
David loves God.
He puts us to shame.
He's so brave.
Such an honour.
Thanks so much ...
but I'm not used to armour.
Although David was only a boy, King Saul gave him his own armour and sent him forth.
David found the armour too heavy and threw it off.
That's why he's fighting.
Did his brothers eat the food?

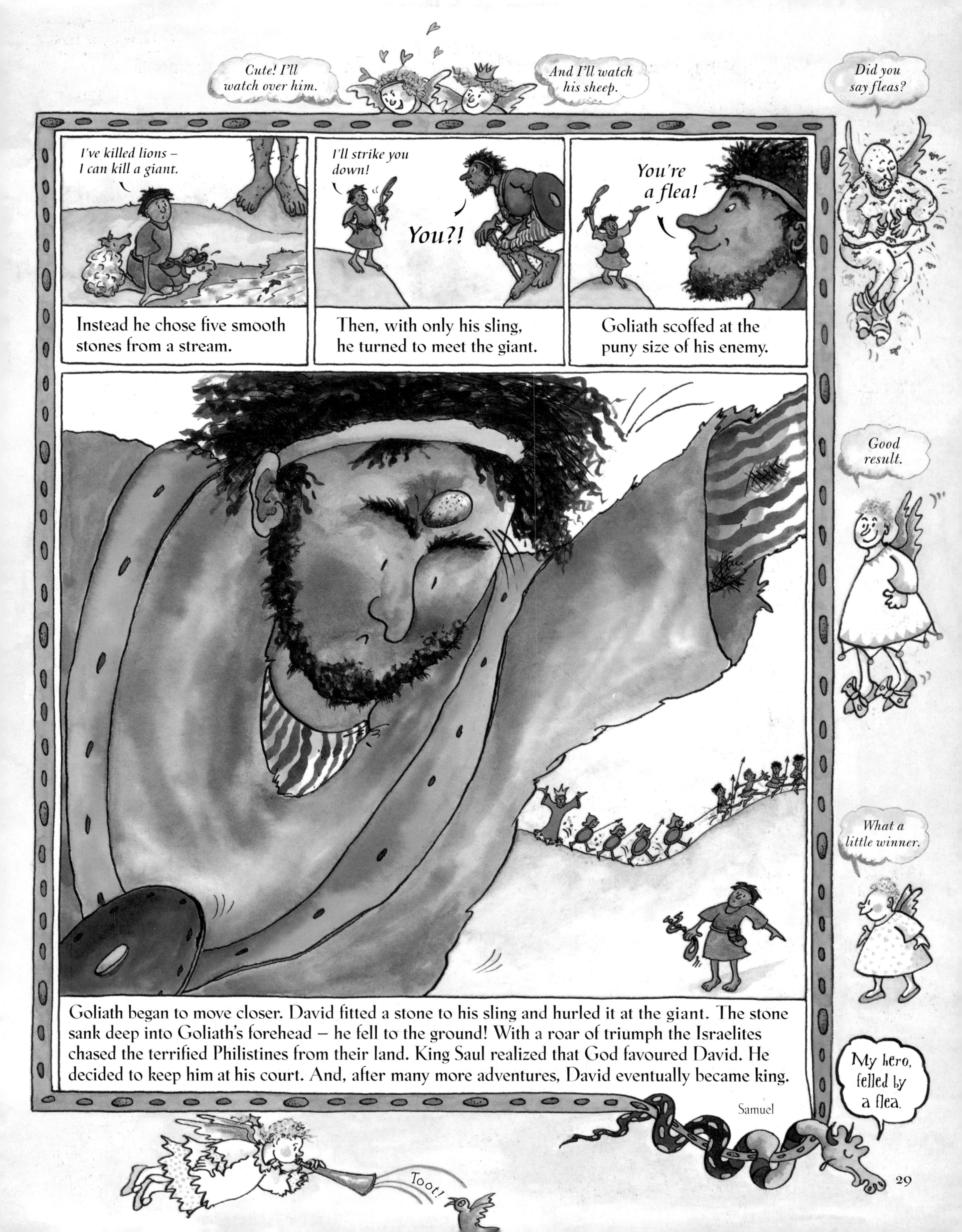

Cute! I'll watch over him.
And I'll watch his sheep.
Did you say fleas?
I've killed lions – I can kill a giant.
Instead he chose five smooth stones from a stream.
I'll strike you down!
You?!
Then, with only his sling, he turned to meet the giant.
You're a flea!
Goliath scoffed at the puny size of his enemy.
Good result.
What a little winner.
Goliath began to move closer. David fitted a stone to his sling and hurled it at the giant. The stone sank deep into Goliath's forehead – he fell to the ground! With a roar of triumph the Israelites chased the terrified Philistines from their land. King Saul realized that God favoured David. He decided to keep him at his court. And, after many more adventures, David eventually became king.
Samuel
My hero, felled by a flea.
Toot!

DANIEL IN THE LIONS' DEN
And so begins another heavenly tale.
Nice catch!
Won't our gods and the king be chuffed!
Daniel was an Israelite from a noble family. When the Babylonians besieged the city of Jerusalem, they seized treasure and took Daniel and three other young nobles to Babylon to serve their king. The Babylonians did not believe in God. They honoured their own gods and goddesses.
God's creatures have no sense!
For you.
No, thanks.
Daniel and his friends were offered rich food and wine.
Vegetables and water will be fine.
Your brains will shrivel!
But they kept God's law and only ate simple food.
You seem quite bright – in spite of the diet!
They were wise young men and soon became royal counsellors.
MMMM!
Good old God!
God had made Daniel the wisest.
I make thee a ruler!
So King Darius made him a state governor.
He'll rule over the whole kingdom soon!
The Babylonian nobles were outraged!
Whisper, whisper, whisper!
They plotted to dishonour Daniel.
Nobles after my own heart!
Now, O King, issue the decree.
OK.
They persuaded the king to say that everyone had to worship him or else be fed to the lions.
Dear God...
As the Babylonian nobles had hoped, Daniel would only worship his God.
Daniel pays no attention to you!
The delighted nobles rushed to inform the king and demand Daniel's punishment.
You have no heart!
But I have a very large heart.

King Darius loved Daniel, but he had to uphold the law of his kingdom. Daniel was thrown into the lions' den. King Darius spent a sleepless night imagining his friend being eaten by the lions.

At the first light of dawn he ran to the den and called out to Daniel. To his amazement, Daniel answered. With the help of an angel, God had shut the mouths of the lions.

The king was overjoyed and declared that all Babylonians should now honour the God of Daniel. The nobles were not pleased.

Daniel

JONAH AND THE GREAT FISH
I'd go to Nineveh for you!
Too high again.
Go to the great city of Nineveh and preach against it.
Nineveh ... me? You're joking? You're not joking!
God wanted people to be kind; when they were cruel he tried to change their ways. He once asked the prophet Jonah to go to Nineveh in Assyria and warn the people against their wickedness.
Ahoy, hold-hard, heave over ... WAIT!
You'll be for it now!
Assyria was the land of Israel's enemy, and Jonah did not want to go. He hurried aboard a ship sailing in the opposite direction. This angered God!
So God sent a terrifying storm that threatened to break up the ship. The wind tore at its sails and the waves crashed against its hull. The ship shuddered and creaked.
He is seriously angry.
Sssplendid! A disobedient prophet.

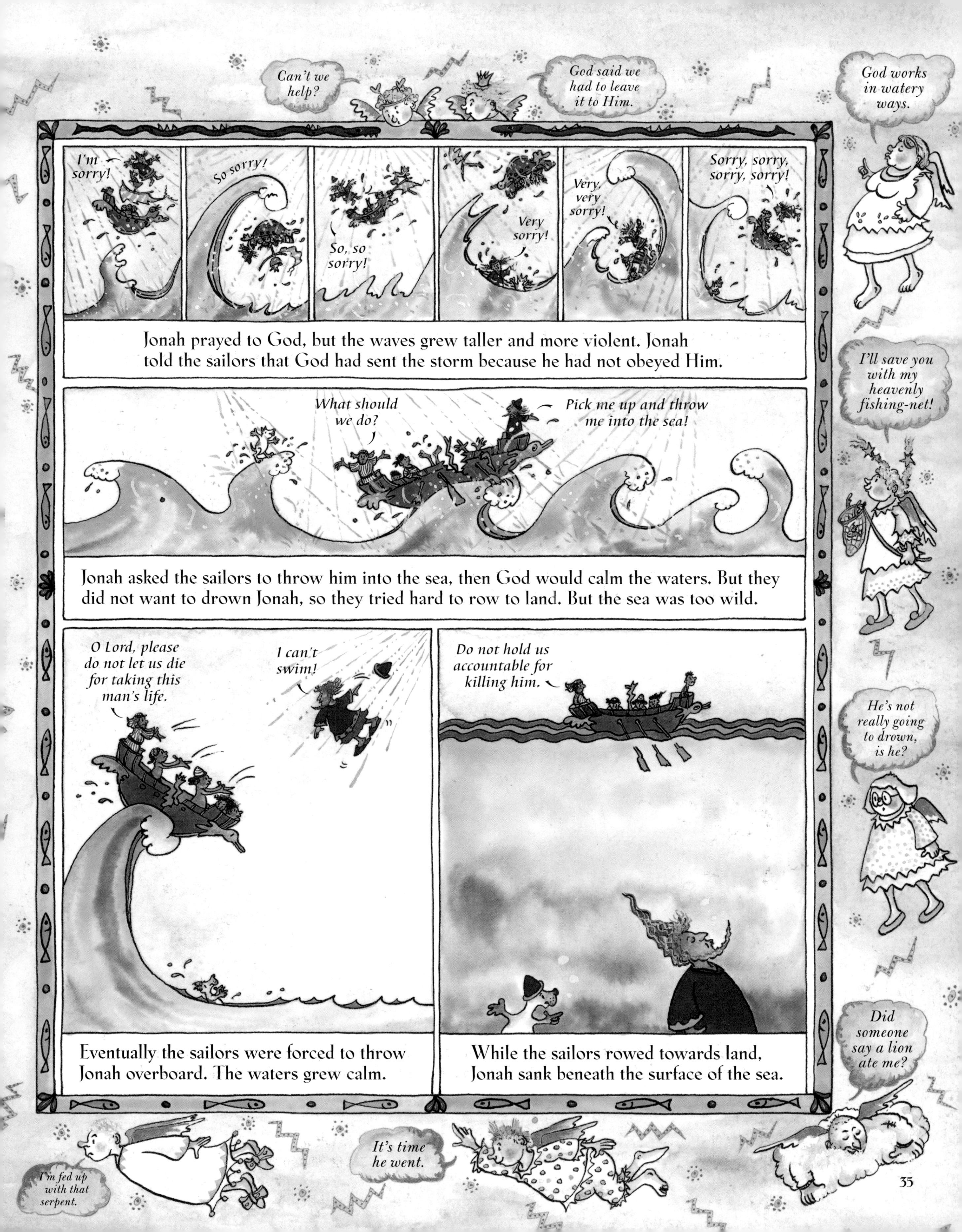
Can't we help?
God said we had to leave it to Him.
God works in watery ways.
I'm sorry!
So sorry!
So, so sorry!
Very sorry!
Very, very sorry!
Sorry, sorry, sorry, sorry!
Jonah prayed to God, but the waves grew taller and more violent. Jonah told the sailors that God had sent the storm because he had not obeyed Him.
I'll save you with my heavenly fishing-net!
What should we do?
Pick me up and throw me into the sea!
Jonah asked the sailors to throw him into the sea, then God would calm the waters. But they did not want to drown Jonah, so they tried hard to row to land. But the sea was too wild.
O Lord, please do not let us die for taking this man's life.
I can't swim!
Do not hold us accountable for killing him.
He's not really going to drown, is he?
Eventually the sailors were forced to throw Jonah overboard. The waters grew calm.
While the sailors rowed towards land, Jonah sank beneath the surface of the sea.
Did someone say a lion ate me?
I'm fed up with that serpent.
It's time he went.

Jonah did not drown, because God sent a great fish to swallow him. He stayed inside the belly of the fish for three days and three nights, praying for God's forgiveness.

I think he's got the message.
But can he deliver the message?
OK, I'm going.
Then God told the fish to vomit Jonah out onto dry land. God again asked Jonah to go to Nineveh and warn the people against their wickedness. This time Jonah went!
Forty more days and Nineveh will be overturned.
In Nineveh, Jonah warned the people that God would destroy their city unless they repented.
Let everyone call urgently on God. Let them give up their evil ways and violence.
The king and Ninevites believed Jonah. They put on sackcloth and turned their backs on evil.
God will be pleased.
I always knew God would relent.
Is that the end?
When God saw that Jonah had changed the minds of the Ninevites He decided to spare Nineveh. Everyone rejoiced and praised God. And God was happy with His creations.
Jonah
Anyone for orb-ball?
You aggravating angelsss. I will be back!

Bless you
my angels,
sleep tight!
You don't
say that in
the Bible!
Sweet dreams.

Goodnight!

Marcia Williams

With her distinctive cartoon-strip style, lively text and brilliant wit, Marcia Williams brings to life some of the world's all-time favourite stories and some colourful historical characters. Her hilarious retellings and clever observations will have children laughing out loud and

coming back for more!

ISBN 978-1-4063-1137-2
ISBN 978-1-4063-1866-1
ISBN 978-1-4063-0563-0
ISBN 978-1-4063-1944-6
ISBN 978-1-4063-2334-4
ISBN 978-1-4063-2335-1
ISBN 978-1-4063-2610-9
ISBN 978-1-4063-0562-3
ISBN 978-1-4063-0171-7
ISBN 978-1-4063-0348-3
ISBN 978-1-4063-0347-6
ISBN 978-1-4063-1002-3
ISBN 978-1-4063-0940-9